Maths Today
for ages 7-8

Addition

Subtraction

Multiplication

Money

Measurement

Time

Halves

Quarters

Shape

Missing numbers

Look at how we can make 6 by adding two numbers together.

6

0 + 6 = 6	6 + 0 = 6
1 + 5 = 6	5 + 1 = 6
2 + 4 = 6	4 + 2 = 6
3 + 3 = 6	

Find all the addition pairs for the numbers shown.

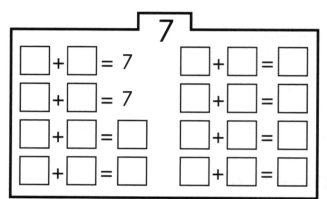

7

$\square + \square = 7$ $\square + \square = \square$
$\square + \square = 7$ $\square + \square = \square$
$\square + \square = \square$ $\square + \square = \square$
$\square + \square = \square$ $\square + \square = \square$

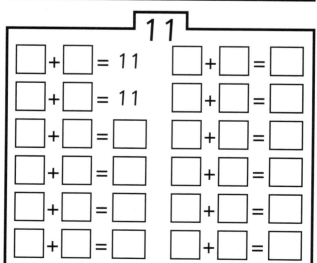

9

$\square + \square = 9$ $\square + \square = \square$
$\square + \square = 9$ $\square + \square = \square$
$\square + \square = \square$ $\square + \square = \square$
$\square + \square = \square$ $\square + \square = \square$
$\square + \square = \square$ $\square + \square = \square$

11

$\square + \square = 11$ $\square + \square = \square$
$\square + \square = 11$ $\square + \square = \square$
$\square + \square = \square$ $\square + \square = \square$
$\square + \square = \square$ $\square + \square = \square$
$\square + \square = \square$ $\square + \square = \square$
$\square + \square = \square$ $\square + \square = \square$

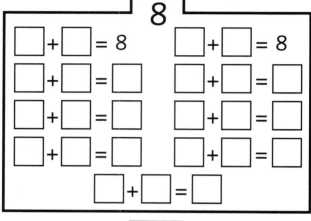

8

$\square + \square = 8$ $\square + \square = 8$
$\square + \square = \square$ $\square + \square = \square$
$\square + \square = \square$ $\square + \square = \square$
$\square + \square = \square$ $\square + \square = \square$
$\square + \square = \square$

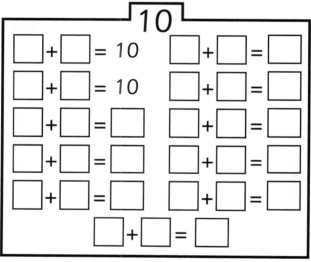

10

$\square + \square = 10$ $\square + \square = \square$
$\square + \square = 10$ $\square + \square = \square$
$\square + \square = \square$ $\square + \square = \square$
$\square + \square = \square$ $\square + \square = \square$
$\square + \square = \square$ $\square + \square = \square$
$\square + \square = \square$

12

$\square + \square = 12$ $\square + \square = \square$
$\square + \square = 12$ $\square + \square = \square$
$\square + \square = \square$ $\square + \square = \square$
$\square + \square = \square$ $\square + \square = \square$
$\square + \square = \square$ $\square + \square = \square$
$\square + \square = \square$ $\square + \square = \square$
$\square + \square = \square$

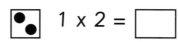
Fill in the missing numbers on the 2 times tables.

1 x 2 = ☐

2 x 2 = ☐

3 x 2 = ☐

4 x 2 = ☐

5 x 2 = ☐

6 x 2 = ☐

7 x 2 = ☐

8 x 2 = ☐

9 x 2 = ☐

10 x 2 = ☐

Use the 2 times table to help you to answer these questions.

18 ÷ 2 = ☐   20 ÷ 2 = ☐

12 ÷ 2 = ☐   4 ÷ 2 = ☐

2 ÷ 2 = ☐   8 ÷ 2 = ☐

14 ÷ 2 = ☐   16 ÷ 2 = ☐

10 ÷ 2 = ☐   6 ÷ 2 = ☐

1) 4 + 6 =

2) 5 + 7 =

3) 9 + 3 =

4) 6 + 5 =

5) 8 + 7 =

6) 9 + 4 =

7) 7 + 7 =

8) 6 + 6 =

9) 8 + 4 =

10) 7 + 8 =

11) 9 + 6 =

12) 8 + 8 =

13) 9 + 5 =

14) 9 + 9 =

15) 9 + 7 =

More missing numbers

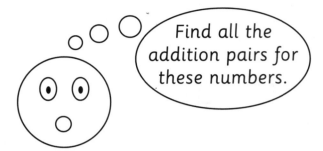

Find all the addition pairs for these numbers.

13

0 + 13 = 13	13 + 0 = 13
1 + 12 = 13	12 + 1 = 13
☐ + ☐ = 13	☐ + ☐ = 13
☐ + ☐ = 13	☐ + ☐ = 13
☐ + ☐ = 13	☐ + ☐ = 13
☐ + ☐ = 13	☐ + ☐ = 13
☐ + ☐ = 13	☐ + ☐ = 13

14

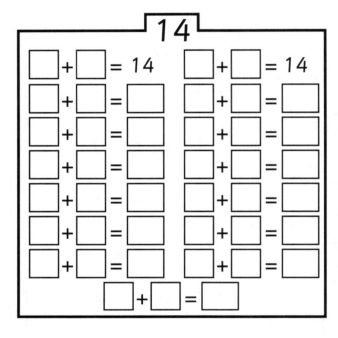

☐ + ☐ = 14	☐ + ☐ = 14
☐ + ☐ = ☐	☐ + ☐ = ☐
☐ + ☐ = ☐	☐ + ☐ = ☐
☐ + ☐ = ☐	☐ + ☐ = ☐
☐ + ☐ = ☐	☐ + ☐ = ☐
☐ + ☐ = ☐	☐ + ☐ = ☐
☐ + ☐ = ☐	☐ + ☐ = ☐
☐ + ☐ = ☐	

15

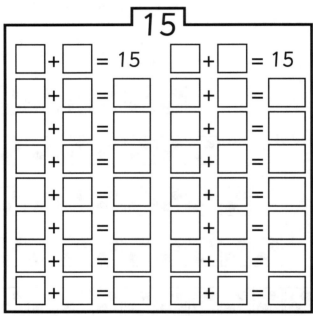

☐ + ☐ = 15	☐ + ☐ = 15
☐ + ☐ = ☐	☐ + ☐ = ☐
☐ + ☐ = ☐	☐ + ☐ = ☐
☐ + ☐ = ☐	☐ + ☐ = ☐
☐ + ☐ = ☐	☐ + ☐ = ☐
☐ + ☐ = ☐	☐ + ☐ = ☐
☐ + ☐ = ☐	☐ + ☐ = ☐
☐ + ☐ = ☐	☐ + ☐ = ☐

16

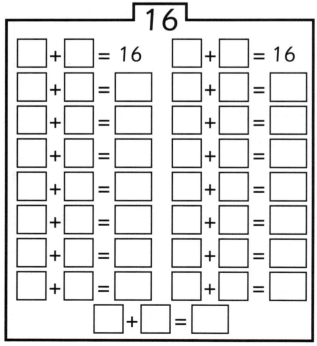

☐ + ☐ = 16	☐ + ☐ = 16
☐ + ☐ = ☐	☐ + ☐ = ☐
☐ + ☐ = ☐	☐ + ☐ = ☐
☐ + ☐ = ☐	☐ + ☐ = ☐
☐ + ☐ = ☐	☐ + ☐ = ☐
☐ + ☐ = ☐	☐ + ☐ = ☐
☐ + ☐ = ☐	☐ + ☐ = ☐
☐ + ☐ = ☐	

17

☐ + ☐ = 17	☐ + ☐ = 17
☐ + ☐ = ☐	☐ + ☐ = ☐
☐ + ☐ = ☐	☐ + ☐ = ☐
☐ + ☐ = ☐	☐ + ☐ = ☐
☐ + ☐ = ☐	☐ + ☐ = ☐
☐ + ☐ = ☐	☐ + ☐ = ☐
☐ + ☐ = ☐	☐ + ☐ = ☐
☐ + ☐ = ☐	☐ + ☐ = ☐
☐ + ☐ = ☐	☐ + ☐ = ☐

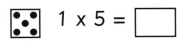

Fill in the missing numbers on the 5 times table.

1 x 5 = ☐

2 x 5 = ☐

3 x 5 = ☐

4 x 5 = ☐

5 x 5 = ☐

6 x 5 = ☐

7 x 5 = ☐

8 x 5 = ☐

9 x 5 = ☐

10 x 5 = ☐

Use the 5 times table to help you to answer these questions.

35 ÷ 5 = ☐   20 ÷ 5 = ☐

5 ÷ 5 = ☐   40 ÷ 5 = ☐

15 ÷ 5 = ☐   10 ÷ 5 = ☐

50 ÷ 5 = ☐   25 ÷ 5 = ☐

45 ÷ 5 = ☐   30 ÷ 5 = ☐

1) 12 + 6 =

2) 16 + 7 =

3) 18 + 4 =

4) 19 + 8 =

5) 17 + 9 =

6) 15 + 5 =

7) 12 + 9 =

8) 13 + 8 =

9) 14 + 7 =

10) 16 + 9 =

11) 19 + 6 =

12) 15 + 9 =

13) 18 + 7 =

14) 17 + 8 =

15) 13 + 9 =

5

Further missing numbers

Find all the addition pairs for these numbers.

18

| 0 + 18 = 18 | 18 + 0 = 18 |
| 1 + 17 = 18 | 17 + 1 = 18 |

☐ + ☐ = 18   ☐ + ☐ = 18

☐ + ☐ = ☐   ☐ + ☐ = ☐

☐ + ☐ = ☐   ☐ + ☐ = ☐

☐ + ☐ = ☐   ☐ + ☐ = ☐

☐ + ☐ = ☐   ☐ + ☐ = ☐

☐ + ☐ = ☐   ☐ + ☐ = ☐

☐ + ☐ = ☐   ☐ + ☐ = ☐

     ☐ + ☐ = ☐

19

☐ + ☐ = 19   ☐ + ☐ = 19

☐ + ☐ = 19   ☐ + ☐ = 19

☐ + ☐ = 19   ☐ + ☐ = 19

☐ + ☐ = ☐   ☐ + ☐ = ☐

☐ + ☐ = ☐   ☐ + ☐ = ☐

☐ + ☐ = ☐   ☐ + ☐ = ☐

☐ + ☐ = ☐   ☐ + ☐ = ☐

☐ + ☐ = ☐   ☐ + ☐ = ☐

☐ + ☐ = ☐   ☐ + ☐ = ☐

20

☐ + ☐ = 20   ☐ + ☐ = 20

☐ + ☐ = 20   ☐ + ☐ = 20

☐ + ☐ = 20   ☐ + ☐ = 20

☐ + ☐ = ☐   ☐ + ☐ = ☐

☐ + ☐ = ☐   ☐ + ☐ = ☐

☐ + ☐ = ☐   ☐ + ☐ = ☐

☐ + ☐ = ☐   ☐ + ☐ = ☐

☐ + ☐ = ☐   ☐ + ☐ = ☐

☐ + ☐ = ☐   ☐ + ☐ = ☐

     ☐ + ☐ = ☐

Fill in the missing numbers in the 10 times table.

Then use the 10 times table to help with these divisions.

1 x 10 = ☐

2 x 10 = ☐

3 x 10 = ☐

4 x 10 = ☐

5 x 10 = ☐

6 x 10 = ☐

7 x 10 = ☐

8 x 10 = ☐

9 x 10 = ☐

10 x 10 = ☐

80 ÷ 10 = ☐

40 ÷ 10 = ☐

10 ÷ 10 = ☐

90 ÷ 10 = ☐

30 ÷ 10 = ☐

60 ÷ 10 = ☐

100 ÷ 10 = ☐

50 ÷ 10 = ☐

20 ÷ 10 = ☐

70 ÷ 10 = ☐

1) 14 + 13 =

2) 12 + 15 =

3) 11 + 16 =

4) 15 + 13 =

5) 16 + 14 =

6) 17 + 12 =

7) 14 + 15 =

8) 13 + 16 =

9) 18 + 11 =

10) 19 + 11 =

11) 17 + 13 =

12) 15 + 15 =

13) 16 + 13 =

14) 12 + 18 =

15) 17 + 11 =

When we multiply by 10 …

… the other digits move to the left and we fill the units space with a zero.

Look: 6 x 10 = 60

units

The 6 has moved to the left

The units space is filled with a zero

Look: 54 x 10 = 540

138 x 10 = 1380

Number facts

+	4	6	3	2	9	8	7	1	5
9					18				
2				4					
6		12							
1								2	
8						16			
4	8								
7							14		
5									10
3			6						

The numbers we've filled in are the doubles.

Double 6 = ☐   Double 3 = ☐   Double 9 = ☐

Double 5 = ☐   Double 8 = ☐

Double 2 = ☐   Double 4 = ☐   Double 7 = ☐

Practise the 3 times table ...

... and the 4 times table.

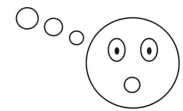

Answer these questions as quickly as you can.

1 x 3 = ☐

2 x 3 = ☐

3 x 3 = ☐

4 x 3 = ☐

5 x 3 = ☐

6 x 3 = ☐

7 x 3 = ☐

8 x 3 = ☐

9 x 3 = ☐

10 x 3 = ☐

1 x 4 = ☐

2 x 4 = ☐

3 x 4 = ☐

4 x 4 = ☐

5 x 4 = ☐

6 x 4 = ☐

7 x 4 = ☐

8 x 4 = ☐

9 x 4 = ☐

10 x 4 = ☐

Now try these divisions.

40 ÷ 4 = ☐

24 ÷ 3 = ☐

12 ÷ 4 = ☐

36 ÷ 4 = ☐

30 ÷ 3 = ☐

18 ÷ 3 = ☐

24 ÷ 4 = ☐

15 ÷ 3 = ☐

27 ÷ 3 = ☐

16 ÷ 4 = ☐

1) 12 – 7 =

2) 14 – 8 =

3) 13 – 6 =

4) 15 – 7 =

5) 16 – 8 =

6) 18 – 9 =

7) 17 – 5 =

8) 12 – 9 =

9) 13 – 8 =

10) 14 – 5 =

11) 16 – 3 =

12) 15 – 9 =

13) 14 – 7 =

14) 13 – 4 =

15) 18 – 6 =

Tens and units

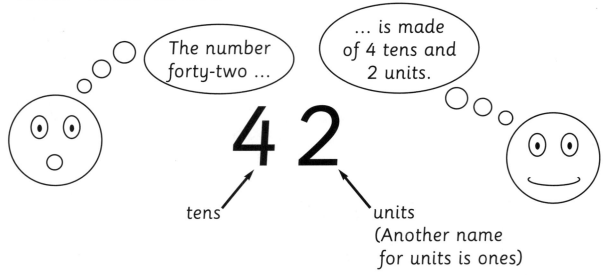

The number forty-two ...

... is made of 4 tens and 2 units.

4 2

tens

units
(Another name for units is ones)

Look:
  T U   U   T U
  4 2 + 5 = 4 7

The tens haven't changed

The units have gone up because 2 + 5 = 7

Look:
  T U   T U   T U
  4 2 + 2 0 = 6 2

There are no units

The units haven't changed

The tens have gone up because 4 tens add 2 tens makes 6 tens

Look:
  T U   T U   T U
  4 2 + 3 6 = 7 8

4 tens add 3 tens makes 7 tens

2 + 6 = 8

Try these additions.

① 53 + 6 = ☐   ② 61 + 7 = ☐

③ 34 + 5 = ☐   ④ 85 + 3 = ☐

⑤ 72 + 7 = ☐   ⑥ 23 + 30 = ☐

⑦ 17 + 40 = ☐   ⑧ 56 + 40 = ☐

⑨ 48 + 30 = ☐   ⑩ 69 + 20 = ☐

⑪ 22 + 25 = ☐   ⑫ 43 + 36 = ☐

⑬ 71 + 28 = ☐   ⑭ 37 + 12 = ☐

Sometimes when we add two numbers together ...

... we get enough units to make an extra ten.

Look:

$$\overset{T\ U}{3\ 7} \ + \ \overset{T\ U}{2\ 5}$$

3 tens add 2 tens makes 5 tens

7 units add 5 units makes 12

12 is 1 ten and 2 units

$$50 \ + \ 12 \ = \ 62$$

Look back at page 7 to find how to do these questions.

1)   6 x 10 =

2)   23 x 10 =

3)   48 x 10 =

4)   56 x 10 =

5)   79 x 10 =

6)   8 x 10 =

7)   92 x 10 =

8)   64 x 10 =

9)   21 x 10 =

10) 85 x 10 =

11) 37 x 10 =

12) 18 x 10 =

13) 116 x 10 =

14) 249 x 10 =

15) 512 x 10 =

Addition and subtraction

Try these additions.

48 + 13 = ☐

57 + 26 = ☐

19 + 15 = ☐

28 + 17 = ☐

36 + 36 = ☐

Now look at these subtractions.

T U   T U   T U

$49 - 8 = 41$

The tens haven't changed

$9 - 8 = 1$

T U   T U   T U

$49 - 30 = 19$

4 tens – 3 tens = 1 ten

$9 - 0 = 9$

T U   T U   T U

$49 - 12 = 37$

4 tens – 1 ten = 3 tens

$9 - 2 = 7$

Try these subtractions.

① 87 − 6 = ☐ ② 98 − 4 = ☐

③ 39 − 5 = ☐ ④ 46 − 3 = ☐

⑤ 77 − 5 = ☐ ⑥ 66 − 20 = ☐

⑦ 51 − 30 = ☐ ⑧ 99 − 60 = ☐

⑨ 86 − 40 = ☐ ⑩ 72 − 50 = ☐

⑪ 87 − 23 = ☐ ⑫ 96 − 41 = ☐

⑬ 75 − 25 = ☐ ⑭ 38 − 17 = ☐

Sometimes we can use a number line to help us to subtract.

We will show you how on page 14.

We will show you how on page 14.

Answer these questions as quickly as you can.

1) Double 2 =

2) Double 6 =

3) Double 8 =

4) Double 5 =

5) Double 3 =

6) Double 10 =

7) Double 9 =

8) Double 7 =

9) Double 4 =

10) Double 12 =

11) Double 15 =

12) Double 11 =

13) Double 18 =

14) Double 16 =

15) Double 13 =

Number lines

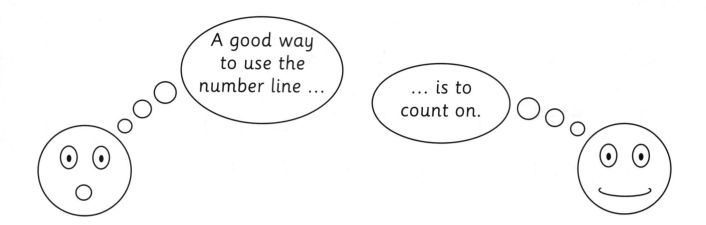

Look: **41 – 28**

Start at the number 28 and count on to the number 41:

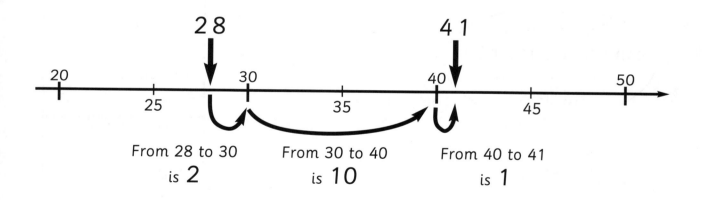

We have counted on **2** and **10** and **1** ...

... so altogether we have counted on **13**.

41 – 28 = 13

Use the number lines to help you with these subtractions.

74 – 48 = ☐

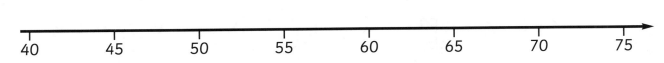

83 – 57 = ☐

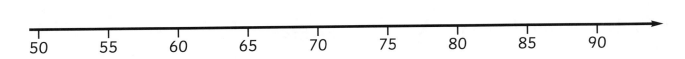

65 – 26 = ☐

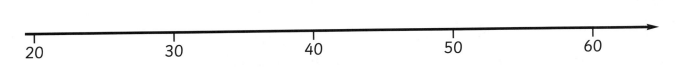

91 – 18 = ☐

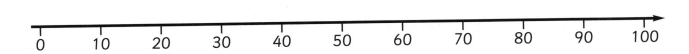

Numbers and words

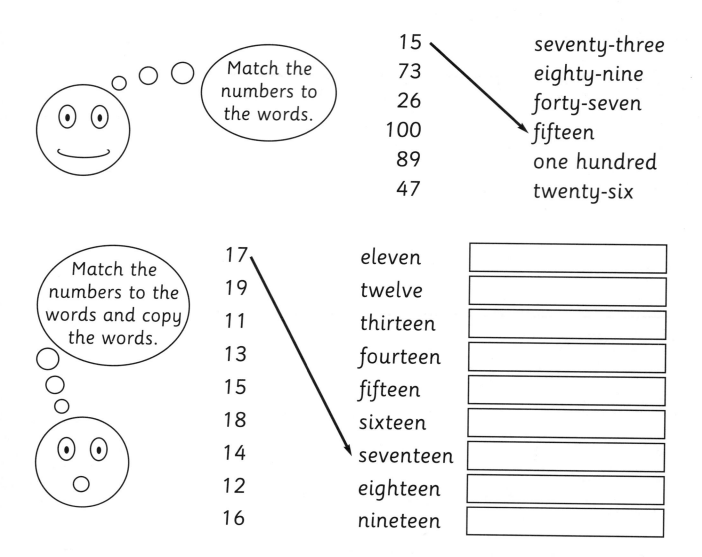

Match the numbers to the words.

15	seventy-three
73	eighty-nine
26	forty-seven
100	fifteen
89	one hundred
47	twenty-six

Match the numbers to the words and copy the words.

17	eleven
19	twelve
11	thirteen
13	fourteen
15	fifteen
18	sixteen
14	seventeen
12	eighteen
16	nineteen

Match then copy the words to practise their spellings.

90	twenty
40	thirty
60	forty
30	fifty
100	sixty
50	seventy
70	eighty
20	ninety
80	one hundred

1 x 5 = ☐
2 x 5 = ☐
3 x 5 = ☐
4 x 5 = ☐
5 x 5 = ☐
6 x 5 = ☐
7 x 5 = ☐
8 x 5 = ☐
9 x 5 = ☐
10 x 5 = ☐

These numbers are multiples of 5

Multiples of 5 ...

... always end in a 5 or a zero.

1 x 10 = ☐
2 x 10 = ☐
3 x 10 = ☐
4 x 10 = ☐
5 x 10 = ☐
6 x 10 = ☐
7 x 10 = ☐
8 x 10 = ☐
9 x 10 = ☐
10 x 10 = ☐

Multiples of 10 always end with a ☐

1 x 2 = ☐
2 x 2 = ☐
3 x 2 = ☐
4 x 2 = ☐
5 x 2 = ☐
6 x 2 = ☐
7 x 2 = ☐
8 x 2 = ☐
9 x 2 = ☐
10 x 2 = ☐

Multiples of 2 always end with 0,2,4,6 or ☐

Answer these questions as quickly as you can.

Write 1 more.

19 ⟶ ☐

39 ⟶ ☐

59 ⟶ ☐

69 ⟶ ☐

99 ⟶ ☐

Write 1 less.

70 ⟶ ☐

30 ⟶ ☐

90 ⟶ ☐

50 ⟶ ☐

200 ⟶ ☐

Write 10 more.

63 ⟶ ☐

21 ⟶ ☐

47 ⟶ ☐

82 ⟶ ☐

91 ⟶ ☐

Coins and money

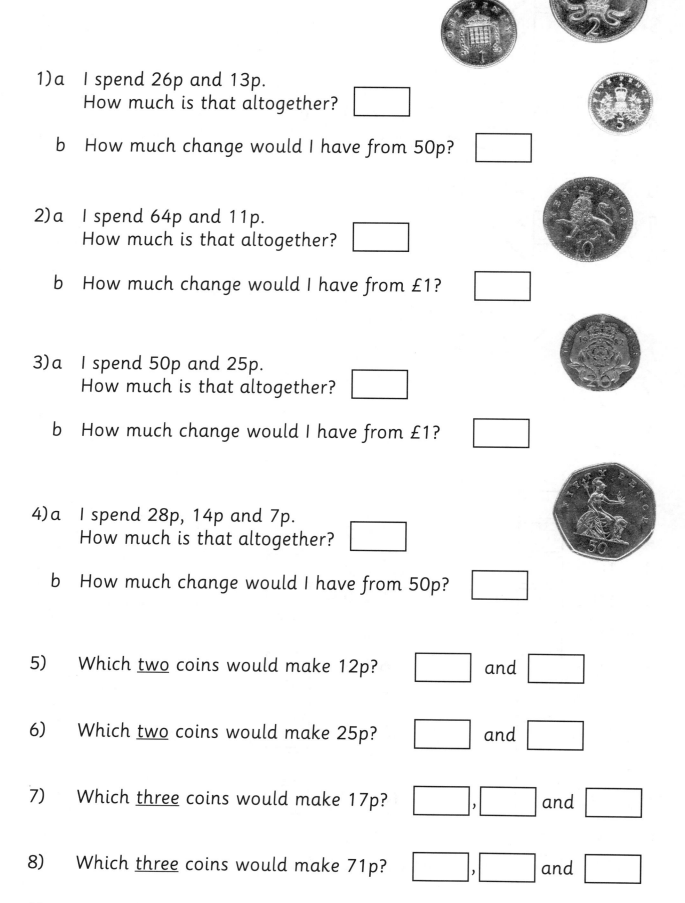

1) a I spend 26p and 13p.
     How much is that altogether? ☐

   b How much change would I have from 50p? ☐

2) a I spend 64p and 11p.
     How much is that altogether? ☐

   b How much change would I have from £1? ☐

3) a I spend 50p and 25p.
     How much is that altogether? ☐

   b How much change would I have from £1? ☐

4) a I spend 28p, 14p and 7p.
     How much is that altogether? ☐

   b How much change would I have from 50p? ☐

5) Which <u>two</u> coins would make 12p? ☐ and ☐

6) Which <u>two</u> coins would make 25p? ☐ and ☐

7) Which <u>three</u> coins would make 17p? ☐ , ☐ and ☐

8) Which <u>three</u> coins would make 71p? ☐ , ☐ and ☐

If I spend thirty-seven pence, how much change would I have from a fifty pence coin?

Thirteen pence.

Write 1 more.

385 → ☐

417 → ☐

842 → ☐

499 → ☐

999 → ☐

Write 1 less.

701 → ☐

218 → ☐

600 → ☐

520 → ☐

870 → ☐

Write 10 less.

960 → ☐

610 → ☐

540 → ☐

700 → ☐

701 → ☐

Amount	Change from 50p
48p	☐
27p	☐
31p	☐
19p	☐
15p	☐

Amount	Change from £1
60p	☐
61p	☐
80p	☐
81p	☐
82p	☐

19

Measuring

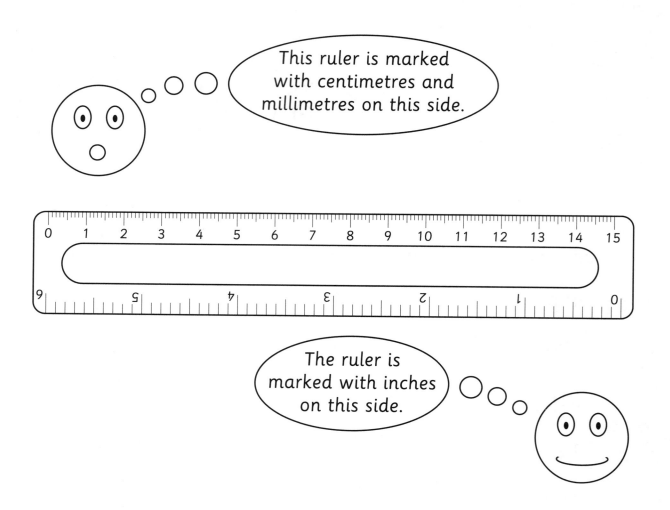

We can use the ruler to measure the length of this black line.

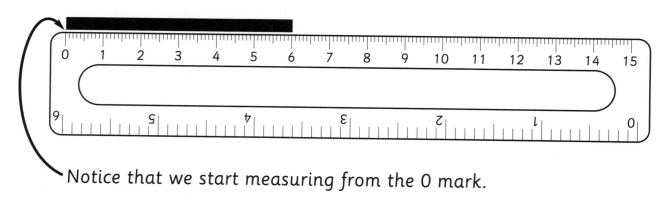

Notice that we start measuring from the 0 mark.

The black line is 6 centimetres long.
We can write 6 centimetres like this: 6 cm

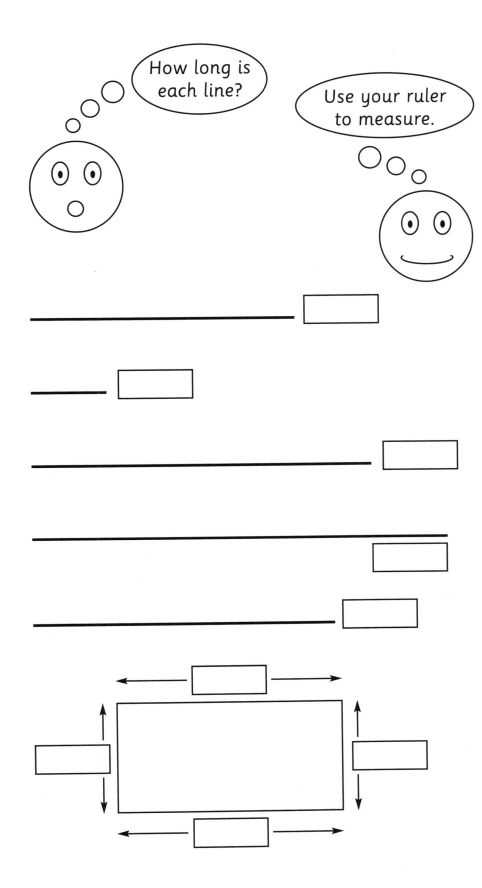

How long is each line?

Use your ruler to measure.

Add the lengths of the sides to find the distance all round the rectangle. This is called the perimeter.

1) 300 + 63 =

2) 500 + 17 =

3) 285 + 3 =

4) 714 + 6 =

5) 423 + 6 =

6) 517 + 7 =

7) 289 + 6 =

8) 325 + 8 =

9) 864 + 9 =

10) 623 + 14 =

11) 916 + 11 =

12) 131 + 13 =

13) 745 + 12 =

14) 482 + 15 =

15) 506 + 21 =

21

Calendar for 2006

January

M	T	W	T	F	S	S
						1
2	3	4	5	6	7	8
9	10	11	12	13	14	15
16	17	18	19	20	21	22
23	24	25	26	27	28	29
30	31					

February

M	T	W	T	F	S	S
		1	2	3	4	5
6	7	8	9	10	11	12
13	14	15	16	17	18	19
20	21	22	23	24	25	26
27	28					

March

M	T	W	T	F	S	S
		1	2	3	4	5
6	7	8	9	10	11	12
13	14	15	16	17	18	19
20	21	22	23	24	25	26
27	28	29	30	31		

April

M	T	W	T	F	S	S
					1	2
3	4	5	6	7	8	9
10	11	12	13	14	15	16
17	18	19	20	21	22	23
24	25	26	27	28	29	30

May

M	T	W	T	F	S	S
1	2	3	4	5	6	7
8	9	10	11	12	13	14
15	16	17	18	19	20	21
22	23	24	25	26	27	28
29	30	31				

June

M	T	W	T	F	S	S
			1	2	3	4
5	6	7	8	9	10	11
12	13	14	15	16	17	18
19	20	21	22	23	24	25
26	27	28	29	30		

July

M	T	W	T	F	S	S
					1	2
3	4	5	6	7	8	9
10	11	12	13	14	15	16
17	18	19	20	21	22	23
24	25	26	27	28	29	30
31						

August

M	T	W	T	F	S	S
1	2	3	4	5	6	
7	8	9	10	11	12	13
14	15	16	17	18	19	20
21	22	23	24	25	26	27
28	29	30	31			

September

M	T	W	T	F	S	S
				1	2	3
4	5	6	7	8	9	10
11	12	13	14	15	16	17
18	19	20	21	22	23	24
25	26	27	28	29	30	

October

M	T	W	T	F	S	S
						1
2	3	4	5	6	7	8
9	10	11	12	13	14	15
16	17	18	19	20	21	22
23	24	25	26	27	28	29
30	31					

November

M	T	W	T	F	S	S
		1	2	3	4	5
6	7	8	9	10	11	12
13	14	15	16	17	18	19
20	21	22	23	24	25	26
27	28	29	30			

December

M	T	W	T	F	S	S
				1	2	3
4	5	6	7	8	9	10
11	12	13	14	15	16	17
18	19	20	21	22	23	24
25	26	27	28	29	30	31

Use the calendar to help you with these questions.

Answer these questions as quickly as you can.

1) What day of the week is 2nd June 2006?

2) What day of the week is 26th January 2006?

3) What day of the week is 1st March 2006?

4) What day of the week is 8th September 2006?

5) What day of the week is 5th January 2006?

6) What is today's date?

In 2006, how many days does each month have?

January ☐   February ☐   March ☐

April ☐   May ☐   June ☐

July ☐   August ☐   September ☐

October ☐   November ☐   December ☐

1) 40 + 30 =

2) 50 + 10 =

3) 60 + 20 =

4) 20 + 20 =

5) 30 + 50 =

6) 50 + 30 =

7) 70 + 20 =

8) 80 + 10 =

9) 90 + 10 =

10) 100 − 40 =

11) 100 − 60 =

12) 100 − 30 =

13) 100 − 50 =

14) 100 − 80 =

15) 100 − 70 =

23

Time

We can write the time in two ways:

25 minutes past
or
2.25

Use two ways to write the times that these clocks show.

24

October   May   January

June   August

March   September   November

April   July

December   February

Write the months in order.

	has 31 days.
	has 28 days, but 29 days in a leap year.
	has 31 days.
	has 30 days.
	has 31 days.
	has 30 days.
	has 31 days.
	has 31 days.
	has 30 days.
	has 31 days.
	has 30 days.
	has 31 days.

1) 600 − 6 =

2) 500 − 4 =

3) 900 − 8 =

4) 700 − 1 =

5) 700 − 2 =

6) 700 − 3 =

7) 700 − 4 =

8) 700 − 5 =

9) 700 − 6 =

10) 700 − 7 =

11) 700 − 8 =

12) 700 − 9 =

13) 700 − 10 =

14) 700 − 20 =

15) 700 − 25 =

More time

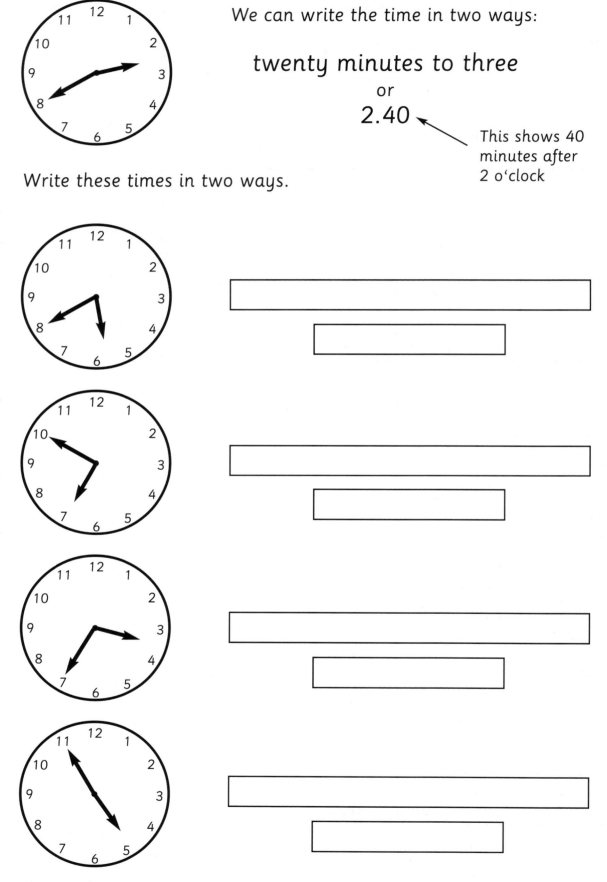

We can write the time in two ways:

twenty minutes to three

or

2.40

This shows 40 minutes after 2 o'clock

Write these times in two ways.

$\frac{1}{2}$ of $4 = 2$

$\frac{1}{2}$ of $5 = 2\frac{1}{2}$

$\frac{1}{2}$ of $6 = \boxed{}$

$\frac{1}{2}$ of $7 = \boxed{}$

$\frac{1}{2}$ of $8 = \boxed{}$

$\frac{1}{2}$ of $9 = \boxed{}$

$\frac{1}{2}$ of $10 = \boxed{}$

Look:

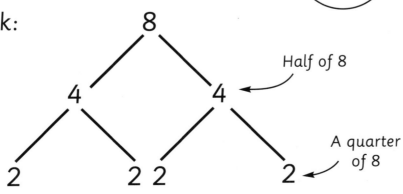

Half of 8

A quarter of 8

1) $100 - 65 =$

2) $100 - 15 =$

3) $100 - 45 =$

4) $100 - 5 =$

5) $100 - 35 =$

6) $100 - 25 =$

7) $100 - 85 =$

8) $100 - 95 =$

9) $100 - 75 =$

10) $100 - 55 =$

11) $100 - 99 =$

12) $100 - 89 =$

13) $100 - 79 =$

14) $100 - 69 =$

15) $100 - 59 =$

Halves and quarters

Split these numbers into halves then quarters.

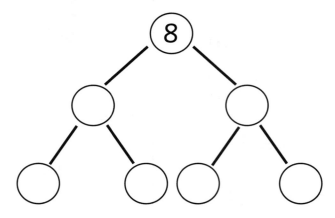

A quarter of 8 is [ ]

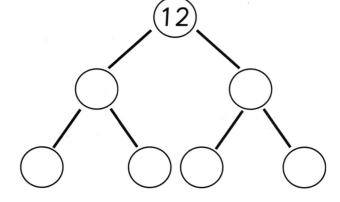

A quarter of 12 is [ ]

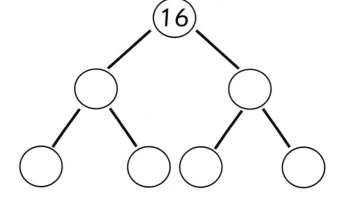

A quarter of 16 is [ ]

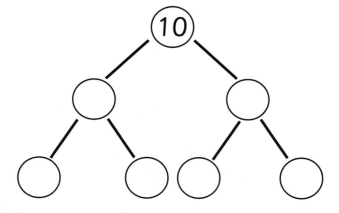

A quarter of 10 is [ ]

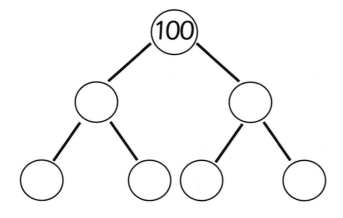

Look at this number line.

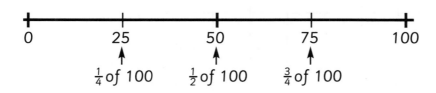

$\frac{1}{4}$ of 100 $\frac{1}{2}$ of 100 $\frac{3}{4}$ of 100

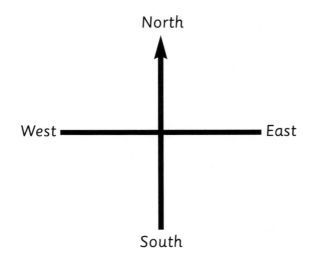

If I face North and turn a quarter turn clockwise I will be facing

If I face North and turn a quarter turn anti-clockwise I will be facing

1) $\frac{1}{2}$ of 6 =

2) $\frac{1}{2}$ of 8 =

3) $\frac{1}{2}$ of 7 =

4) $\frac{1}{2}$ of 4 =

5) $\frac{1}{2}$ of 2 =

6) $\frac{1}{2}$ of 5 =

7) $\frac{1}{2}$ of 9 =

8) $\frac{1}{2}$ of 12 =

9) $\frac{1}{2}$ of 10 =

10) $\frac{1}{2}$ of 11 =

11) $\frac{1}{2}$ of 20 =

12) $\frac{1}{2}$ of 40 =

13) $\frac{1}{2}$ of 30 =

14) $\frac{1}{2}$ of 100 =

15) $\frac{1}{2}$ of 50 =

Shapes

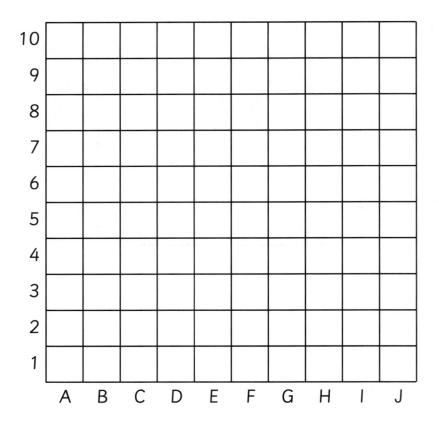

Colour these squares blue: B5, B6, B7, B8, C2, C5, C9, D8, E2, E7, G2, G7, H8, I2, I5, I9, J5, J6, J7, J8

Colour these squares pink: C6, C7, D6, E3, E4, G3, G4, H6, I6, I7

Colour these squares yellow: D3, D4, H3, H4

Colour these squares green: C8, D5, D7, E5, E6, G5, G6, H5, H7, I8

Colour these squares orange: C3, D1, D2, H1, H2, I3

Colour these squares black: F3, F4, F5, F6

What does this pattern remind you of?

Write the correct word on each shape.

WORDS

octagon

triangle

circle

square

hexagon

rectangle

pentagon

semi-circle

1) 3 x 2 =

2) 4 x 5 =

3) 7 x 10 =

4) 6 x 3 =

5) 5 x 4 =

6) 7 x 5 =

7) 9 x 2 =

8) 6 x 5 =

9) 7 x 2 =

10) 5 x 5 =

11) 8 x 2 =

12) 3 x 10 =

13) 6 x 2 =

14) 9 x 5 =

15) 8 x 5 =

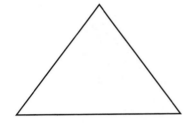

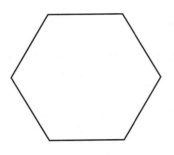

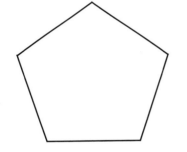

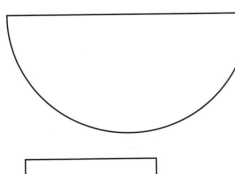

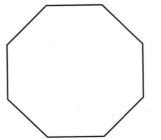

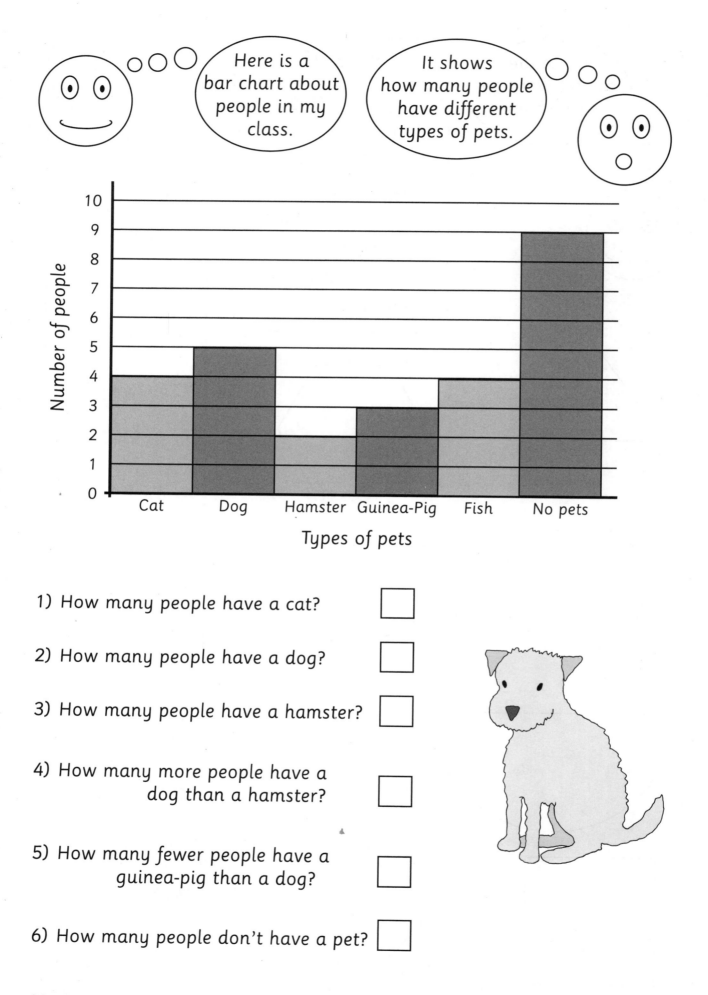

1) How many people have a cat? ☐

2) How many people have a dog? ☐

3) How many people have a hamster? ☐

4) How many more people have a
   dog than a hamster? ☐

5) How many fewer people have a
   guinea-pig than a dog? ☐

6) How many people don't have a pet? ☐